Bedfordshire & Hertfordshire

Edited By Megan Roberts

First published in Great Britain in 2019 by:

Young Writers
Remus House
Coltsfoot Drive
Peterborough
PE2 9BF
Telephone: 01733 890066
Website: www.youngwriters.co.uk

FOREWORD

Dear Reader,

Are you ready to get your thinking caps on to puzzle your way through this wonderful collection?

Young Writers are proud to introduce our new poetry competition, *My First Riddle*, designed to introduce Reception pupils to the delights of poetry. Riddles are a great way to introduce children to the use of poetic expression, including description, similes and expanded noun phrases, as well as encouraging them to 'think outside the box' by providing clues without giving the answer away immediately. Some pupils were given a series of riddle templates to choose from, giving them a framework within which to shape their ideas.

Their answers could be whatever or whoever their imaginations desired; from people to places, animals to objects, food to seasons. All of us here at Young Writers believe in the importance of inspiring young children to produce creative writing, including poetry, and we feel that seeing their own riddles in print will ignite that spark of creativity.

We hope you enjoy riddling your way through this book as much as we enjoyed reading all the entries.

CONTENTS

Ardley Hill Academy, Dunstable

Annie Rudy (5)	1
Elliott Law (4)	2
Charlie Simner (4)	3
Ruby Salmon (4)	4
Emma Sommarvia (5)	5
Nathan Powell (4)	6
Jason Martyn King (4)	7
Lucas Flynn (4)	8
Jenson Chalkley (4)	9
Gracie-Belle Berry (4)	10
Freya Frogell (4)	11
Riley Williams (4)	12
N B (4)	13
Ethan George (4)	14
Siana Roberts (4)	15
Oscar Batham (5)	16
Charlie Williams (4)	17
Laura Konichal (4)	18
Mylo Warner (5)	19
Lucy Nicol (5)	20
Kayden Deery (4)	21
Katie Summer Smith (5)	22
Jayla Johnson (5)	23

Dewhurst Primary School, Cheshunt

Eden Nobrega-Asfaw (5)	24
Priya Barton (5)	25
Amelia Robyn Keys (5)	26
Harry-Bear Martin-Burton (4)	27
Alicia Hajdarmataj (4)	28
David Bieniek (5)	29
Alexander Tsourou (5)	30

Juan Alejandro Barrera Parris (4)	31
Preston Yearwood (5)	32

Peartree Spring Primary School, Stevenage

Amir Abdelnaby (5)	33
Fraser Bowie McKenzie (4)	34
Lucas Iacob (4)	35
Evie Walters (5)	36
Scarlett Crawley (4)	37
Ben Harding (4)	38
Zak Brown (4)	39
Sophie Harris (4)	40
Joshua Smith (4)	41
Chloe Brain (4)	42
Jude James Almond (5)	43
Harry Williams (4)	44
Harrison Banks (5)	45
Jovanni Richardson (4)	46
Joshua Cinar Francisco (4)	47
Noah Garbutt (4)	48
Daniel Tupman (4)	49
Hazel Rose Hurley (4)	50
Ronnie Wicks (4)	51
Dylan O'Driscoll (4)	52
Alfie Stevens (4)	53
Charlotte Florence Neal (4)	54
Jake Knight (4)	55
Brogan Williams (5)	56
Jaden Grose (5)	57
Mollie Doman (5)	58
Victor Andrei Marin (5)	59
Lily Pestana (4)	60
Mia Ramus (4)	61
Erin Usher (5)	62

Blake Bourn (4)	63
Phoebe Harrison (4)	64
Noah Henry Shadbolt (4)	65
Sophia Lily Sabini (4)	66
Lydia Carter (4)	67
Colby Bridle (5)	68
Jaycob Michael Milburn (4)	69
Frederick Wise (5)	70
Maddison Dean (4)	71
Alfie George Green (4)	72
Maisie Chappell (4)	73
Arabella Garcia-Sevilla (5)	74

Robert Peel Primary School, Sandy

Jamie Stokoe (5)	75
Jackson Harper (5)	76
Jackson Scheibner (4)	77
Katie Nemec Vencelova (5)	78
Liam Kyle Shaw-Chung (5)	79
Dotty Reading (5)	80
Ellie Barton (5)	81
Sophia Elizabeth Hurren (5)	82
Lucas English (5)	83
Billy Fry (5)	84
George Powell-Perry (4)	85
Henry Akhurst (5)	86
Ernie Eastwood-Ogawa (4)	87
Autumn Briggs (5)	88
Bethanie Short (5)	89
Kian Rogan (5)	90
Lewis Geeson-Orsgood (5)	91
Elsie Rowley (5)	92
Penny Wallace (4)	93
Kaitlyn Merrett (4)	94
Kai James Parks (5)	95
Ebony Chalkley (5)	96
Ashlee Fielding (5)	97
Tanya Lovett (5)	98
Mylo James Darrington (4)	99
Rylee Bayford (4)	100
Max Xander Whytock (5)	101
Devon Huckle (5)	102

Jace Quan (5)	103
Chloe Louise Butler (5)	104
Marley Berney (4)	105
Jack Quan (5)	106
Luca Gatti (4)	107

Sheerhatch Primary School, Willington

Henry Amies (5)	108
Phoebe Rae Clark (4)	109
Olivia Rodgers (4)	110
Oliver Anderson (5)	111
Ginny Fitzgerald (5)	112
Grace Mary Beales (5)	113

St Bartholomew's CE Primary School, Wiggington

Mathilda Walters (4)	114
Jessica Cubitt (4)	115
Amelie Ryan-Clark (5)	116
Tia Arthur (4)	117
Carlton Maclaughlin (5)	118
Catherine Reading-Burgos (5)	119
Polly Goodman (5)	120
Jessica Beeley (5)	121
Ollie White (4)	122
Euan Rhys-Davies (5)	123
Oscar Peter Cadman (4)	124

St Mary's Infant School, Baldock

Jess Limburn (5)	125
Mercedes Woods (5)	126
Albie Cardall (4)	127
Freddie Rowe (4)	128
Edith Lewis (5)	129
James Taylor (5)	130
Evie Jane Fleming-Smales (5)	131

THE
RIDDLES

Annie's First Riddle

What could it be?
Follow the clues and see.

It looks like **chocolate**.
It sounds like **crunchy chocolate**.
It smells like **sweet flavours**.
It feels like **fluff and snow**.
It tastes like **sweet chocolate**.

Have you guessed what it could be?
Look below and you will see,
It is...

Answer: Penguin chocolate.

Annie Rudy (5)
Ardley Hill Academy, Dunstable

Elliott's First Riddle

What could it be?
Follow the clues and see.

It looks like **white balls**.
It sounds like **an animal's coming**.
It smells like **penguins**.
It feels **furry, squishy, it's cold**.
It tastes like **jam on toast**.

Have you guessed what it could be?
Look below and you will see,
It is...

Answer: Snow.

Elliott Law (4)
Ardley Hill Academy, Dunstable

Charlie's First Riddle

What could it be?
Follow the clues and see.

It looks like **lots of rides**.
It sounds like **motorbikes**.
It smells like **chicken and chips**.
It feels **very cool**.
It tastes like **yummy ice cream**.

Have you guessed what it could be?
Look below and you will see,
It is...

Answer: **Butlins**.

Charlie Simner (4)
Ardley Hill Academy, Dunstable

Ruby's First Riddle

What could it be?
Follow the clues and see.

It looks like **two antlers**.
It sounds like **a neigh**.
It smells like **Santa**.
It feels like **teddies**.
It tastes like **yoghurt**.

Have you guessed what it could be?
Look below and you will see,
It is...

Answer: A reindeer.

Ruby Salmon (4)
Ardley Hill Academy, Dunstable

Emma's First Riddle

What could it be?
Follow the clues and see.

It looks like **a cow.**
It sounds like **a quack.**
It smells like **fish.**
It feels like **a soft jumper.**
It tastes like **a Penguin chocolate bar.**

Have you guessed what it could be?
Look below and you will see,
It is...

Answer: A penguin.

Emma Sommarvia (5)
Ardley Hill Academy, Dunstable

Nathan's First Riddle

What could it be?
Follow the clues and see.

It looks like **peanut butter**.
It sounds like **eating**.
It smells like **orange juice**.
It feels like **apples**.
It tastes like **watermelon**.

Have you guessed what it could be?
Look below and you will see,
It is...

Answer: Strawberries.

Nathan Powell (4)
Ardley Hill Academy, Dunstable

Jason's First Riddle

What could it be?
Follow the clues and see.

It looks like **a person**.
It sounds like **'ooo' and 'aah'**.
It smells like **trees**.
It feels **soft**.
It tastes like **cooking**.

Have you guessed what it could be?
Look below and you will see,
It is...

Answer: A monkey.

Jason Martyn King (4)
Ardley Hill Academy, Dunstable

Lucas' First Riddle

What could it be?
Follow the clues and see.

It looks like **a bit of chicken**.
It sounds like **nothing**.
It smells **yummy**.
It feels **bumpy**.
It tastes like **a bit of chicken**.

Have you guessed what it could be?
Look below and you will see,
It is...

Answer: Chicken nuggets.

Lucas Flynn (4)
Ardley Hill Academy, Dunstable

Jenson's First Riddle

What could it be?
Follow the clues and see.

It looks like **red circles**.
It sounds like **nothing**.
It smells like **tomato sauce**.
It feels **fluffy**.
It tastes like **mayonnaise**.

Have you guessed what it could be?
Look below and you will see,
It is...

Answer: Tomatoes.

Jenson Chalkley (4)
Ardley Hill Academy, Dunstable

Gracie-Belle's First Riddle

What could it be?
Follow the clues and see.

It looks like **tomatoes**.
It sounds like **roast beef**.
It smells like **ketchup**.
It feels like **flowers**.
It tastes like **leaves**.

Have you guessed what it could be?
Look below and you will see,
It is...

Answer: Lasagne.

Gracie-Belle Berry (4)
Ardley Hill Academy, Dunstable

Freya's First Riddle

What could it be?
Follow the clues and see.

It looks like **little circles**.
It sounds **a bit noisy**.
It smells like **stars**.
It feels **chewy**.
It tastes like **strawberries**.

Have you guessed what it could be?
Look below and you will see,
It is...

Answer: *Sweeties.*

Freya Frogell (4)
Ardley Hill Academy, Dunstable

Riley's First Riddle

What could it be?
Follow the clues and see.

It looks like **a bear**.
It sounds like **a monster**.
It smells like **apples**.
It feels **fluffy**.
It tastes like **watermelon**.

Have you guessed what it could be?
Look below and you will see,
It is...

Answer: A teddy bear.

Riley Williams (4)
Ardley Hill Academy, Dunstable

My First Riddle

What could it be?
Follow the clues and see.

It looks like **a tangerine**.
It sounds like **a shaker**.
It smells like **an apple**.
It feels **smooth**.
It tastes like **squash**.

Have you guessed what it could be?
Look below and you will see,
It is...

Answer: Oranges.

N B (4)
Ardley Hill Academy, Dunstable

Ethan's First Riddle

What could it be?
Follow the clues and see.

It is **white and black**.
It sounds like **a station**.
It smells like **wee**.
It feels like **a chicken**.
It tastes like **cheese**.

Have you guessed what it could be?
Look below and you will see,
It is...

Answer: A panda.

Ethan George (4)
Ardley Hill Academy, Dunstable

Siana's First Riddle

What could it be?
Follow the clues and see.

It looks like **silver**.
It sounds like **trump, trump**.
It smells like **mud**.
It feels **soft**.
It tastes **yucky**.

Have you guessed what it could be?
Look below and you will see,
It is...

Answer: An elephant.

Siana Roberts (4)
Ardley Hill Academy, Dunstable

Oscar's First Riddle

What could it be?
Follow the clues and see.

It looks like **white powder**.
It sounds like **a crunch**.
It smells like **vinegar**.
It feels like **cold ice**.
It tastes **yucky**.

Have you guessed what it could be?
Look below and you will see,
It is...

Answer: *Snow.*

Oscar Batham (5)
Ardley Hill Academy, Dunstable

Charlie's First Riddle

What could it be?
Follow the clues and see.

It looks like **pasta and meat**.
It sounds like **popping**.
It smells **delicious**.
It feels **soft**.
It tastes like **meat**.

Have you guessed what it could be?
Look below and you will see,
It is...

Answer: Lasagne.

Charlie Williams (4)
Ardley Hill Academy, Dunstable

Laura's First Riddle

What could it be?
Follow the clues and see.

It looks **fluffy**.
It sounds **scary**.
It smells like **flowers**.
It feels **soft**.
It tastes, **ew! Very disgusting!**.

Have you guessed what it could be?
Look below and you will see,
It is...

Answer: A polar bear.

Laura Konichal (4)
Ardley Hill Academy, Dunstable

18

Mylo's First Riddle

What could it be?
Follow the clues and see.

It looks like **a killer whale**.
It sounds like **a duck**.
It smells **yucky**.
It feels **soft**.
It tastes like **fur**.

Have you guessed what it could be?
Look below and you will see,
It is...

Answer: A penguin.

Mylo Warner (5)
Ardley Hill Academy, Dunstable

Lucy's First Riddle

What could it be?
Follow the clues and see.

It looks like **a gopher**.
It sounds like *miaow*.
It smells like **milk**.
It feels **soft**.
It tastes **hairy**.

Have you guessed what it could be?
Look below and you will see,
It is...

Answer: A cat.

Lucy Nicol (5)
Ardley Hill Academy, Dunstable

Kayden's First Riddle

What could it be?
Follow the clues and see.

It is **green**.
It sounds like **a roar**.
It smells **dirty**.
It feels **strong**.
It doesn't taste **nice**.

Have you guessed what it could be?
Look below and you will see,
It is...

Answer: *The Hulk.*

Kayden Deery (4)
Ardley Hill Academy, Dunstable

Katie's First Riddle

What could it be?
Follow the clues and see.

It looks like **circles**.
It sounds **crunchy**.
It smells **delicious**.
It feels **soft**.
It tastes like **chicken**.

Have you guessed what it could be?
Look below and you will see,
It is...

Answer: Pie.

Katie Summer Smith (5)
Ardley Hill Academy, Dunstable

Jayla's First Riddle

What could it be?
Follow the clues and see.

It looks **white**.
It sounds like **tigers**.
It smells **yucky**.
It feels **soft**.
It tastes **hairy**.

Have you guessed what it could be?
Look below and you will see,
It is...

Answer: A polar bear.

Jayla Johnson (5)
Ardley Hill Academy, Dunstable

Eden's First Riddle

What could it be?
Follow the clues and see.

It looks like **a white horse with a horn.**
It sounds like **a magical neigh.**
It smells like **beautiful perfume.**
It feels like **a soft rainbow teddy.**
It tastes like **candy sticks and marshmallow.**

Have you guessed what it could be?
Look below and you will see,
It is...

Answer: A unicorn.

Eden Nobrega-Asfaw (5)
Dewhurst Primary School, Cheshunt

Priya's First Riddle

What could it be?
Follow the clues and see.

It looks like **a chocolate-covered 'L'.**
It smells like **muddy puddles.**
It feels like **something you rub out with.**
It sounds like **a splish-splosh.**

Have you guessed what it could be?
Look below and you will see,
It is...

Answer: **Welly boots.**

Priya Barton (5)
Dewhurst Primary School, Cheshunt

Amelia's First Riddle

What could it be?
Follow the clues and see.

It looks like **a sphere, nice and round.**
It sounds **crunchy.**
It smells **sweet.**
It feels **sticky and hard.**
It tastes like **a strawberry.**

Have you guessed what it could be?
Look below and you will see,
It is...

Answer: A lollipop.

Amelia Robyn Keys (5)
Dewhurst Primary School, Cheshunt

Harry-Bear's First Riddle

What could it be?
Follow the clues and see.

It looks **blue and shiny**.
It sounds like *splish, splash*.
It smells like **fish**.
It feels **cold and wet**.
It tastes like **salt**.

Have you guessed what it could be?
Look below and you will see,
It is...

Answer: *The sea.*

Harry-Bear Martin-Burton (4)
Dewhurst Primary School, Cheshunt

Alicia's First Riddle

What could it be?
Follow the clues and see.

It looks like **a ball that's red and shiny.**
It sounds **crunchy.**
It smells **fresh.**
It feels **smooth.**
It tastes **juicy.**

Have you guessed what it could be?
Look below and you will see,
It is...

Answer: An apple.

Alicia Hajdarmataj (4)
Dewhurst Primary School, Cheshunt

David's First Riddle

What could it be?
Follow the clues and see.

It looks like **a bear**.
It sounds like **a bear**.
It smells like **strawberry**.
It feels **soft**.
It tastes like **strawberry**.

Have you guessed what it could be?
Look below and you will see,
It is...

Answer: Lotso Bear.

David Bieniek (5)
Dewhurst Primary School, Cheshunt

Alexander's First Riddle

What could it be?
Follow the clues and see.

It looks like **a pet**.
It sounds like **it has four legs**.
It smells like **grass**.
It feels **fluffy**.
It tastes like **a mouse**.

Have you guessed what it could be?
Look below and you will see,
It is...

Answer: A cat.

Alexander Tsourou (5)
Dewhurst Primary School, Cheshunt

Juan's First Riddle

What could it be?
Follow the clues and see.

It looks like **the moon**.
It sounds like **a bang**.
It smells like **air**.
It feels like **a balloon**.
It tastes like **dirt**.

Have you guessed what it could be?
Look below and you will see,
It is...

Answer: A ball.

Juan Alejandro Barrera Parris (4)
Dewhurst Primary School, Cheshunt

Preston's First Riddle

What could it be?
Follow the clues and see.

It looks like **a circle**.
It smells like **chocolate**.
It feels like **a cake**.
It tastes like **oranges**.

Have you guessed what it could be?
Look below and you will see,
It is...

Answer: A Jaffa Cake.

Preston Yearwood (5)
Dewhurst Primary School, Cheshunt

Amir's First Riddle

What could it be?
Follow the clues and see.

It looks like **a big, sandy desert**.
It sounds like **the seagulls**.
It smells like **salty water**.
It feels like **hot sand**.
It tastes like **ice cream**.

Have you guessed what it could be?
Look below and you will see,
It is...

Answer: *The seaside.*

Amir Abdelnaby (5)

Peartree Spring Primary School, Stevenage

Fraser's First Riddle

What could it be?
Follow the clues and see.

It looks like **sand**.
It sounds like **seagulls squawking**.
It smells like **ice cream**.
It feels like **soft waves**.
It tastes like **sandwiches**.

Have you guessed what it could be?
Look below and you will see,
It is...

Answer: *The seaside.*

Fraser Bowie McKenzie (4)
Peartree Spring Primary School, Stevenage

Lucas' First Riddle

What could it be?
Follow the clues and see.

It looks like **a big tower**.
It sounds like **a dinosaur's roar**.
It smells like **smoke**.
It feels **so hot**.
It tastes like **toast**.

Have you guessed what it could be?
Look below and you will see,
It is...

Answer: A volcano.

Lucas Iacob (4)
Peartree Spring Primary School, Stevenage

Evie's First Riddle

What could it be?
Follow the clues and see.

She looks like **yellow hair**.
She sounds like **a human**.
She smells like **clothes**.
She feels **squishy**.
She tastes like **skin**.

Have you guessed who she could be?
Look below and you will see,
She is...

Answer: Evie.

Evie Walters (5)
Peartree Spring Primary School, Stevenage

Scarlett's First Riddle

What could it be?
Follow the clues and see.

It looks like **a big shop**.
It sounds **noisy**.
It smells like **strawberries**.
It feels like **cold ice**.
It tastes like **raspberries**.

Have you guessed what it could be?
Look below and you will see,
It is...

Answer: Asda.

Scarlett Crawley (4)
Peartree Spring Primary School, Stevenage

Ben's First Riddle

What could it be?
Follow the clues and see.

He looks like **a round belly.**
He sounds like **ho, ho, ho.**
He smells like **mince pies.**
He feels **fluffy.**
He tastes like **carrots.**

Have you guessed who he could be?
Look below and you will see,
He is...

Answer: Santa.

Ben Harding (4)
Peartree Spring Primary School, Stevenage

Zak's First Riddle

What could it be?
Follow the clues and see.

It looks like **snow**.
It sounds like **Christmas music**.
It smells **nice**.
It feels **cold**.
It tastes like **sausages**.

Have you guessed what it could be?
Look below and you will see,
It is...

Answer: A **winter** wonderland.

Zak Brown (4)
Peartree Spring Primary School, Stevenage

Sophie's First Riddle

What could it be?
Follow the clues and see.

It looks like **waves**.
It sounds like **seagulls**.
It smells **like salt**.
It feels like **sand**.
It tastes like **sandwiches**.

Have you guessed what it could be?
Look below and you will see,
It is...

Answer: *The beach.*

Sophie Harris (4)
Peartree Spring Primary School, Stevenage

Joshua's First Riddle

What could it be?
Follow the clues and see.

It looks like **hot sand**.
It sounds like **the sea**.
It smells like **ice cream**.
It feels **hot**.
It tastes like **doughnuts**.

Have you guessed what it could be?
Look below and you will see,
It is...

Answer: The beach.

Joshua Smith (4)
Peartree Spring Primary School, Stevenage

Chloe's First Riddle

What could it be?
Follow the clues and see.

It looks like **a house**.
It sounds like **talking**.
It smells **plain**.
It feels **hard**.
It tastes like **sweets**.

Have you guessed what it could be?
Look below and you will see,
It is...

Answer: A Barbie Dream House.

Chloe Brain (4)
Peartree Spring Primary School, Stevenage

Jude's First Riddle

What could it be?
Follow the clues and see.

It looks like **yellow sand**.
It sounds like **waves**.
It smells like **salt**.
It feels **soft**.
It tastes like **ice cream**.

Have you guessed what it could be?
Look below and you will see,
It is...

Answer: *The beach.*

Jude James Almond (5)
Peartree Spring Primary School, Stevenage

Harry's First Riddle

What could it be?
Follow the clues and see.

It looks like **hot sand**.
It sounds like **waves**.
It smells like **salty waves**.
It feels **hot**.
It tastes like **ice cream**.

Have you guessed what it could be?
Look below and you will see,
It is...

Answer: Cyprus.

Harry Williams (4)
Peartree Spring Primary School, Stevenage

Harrison's First Riddle

What could it be?
Follow the clues and see.

It looks **red**.
It sounds like **ho, ho, ho**.
It smells like **Christmas**.
It feels **squishy**.
It tastes like **milk and pie**.

Have you guessed what it could be?
Look below and you will see,
It is...

Answer: *Santa.*

Harrison Banks (5)
Peartree Spring Primary School, Stevenage

Jovanni's First Riddle

What could it be?
Follow the clues and see.

It looks **red and green**.
It sounds like **hissing**.
It smells like **nothing**.
It feels **scaly**.
It tastes like **chicken**.

Have you guessed what it could be?
Look below and you will see,
It is...

Answer: A snake.

Jovanni Richardson (4)
Peartree Spring Primary School, Stevenage

Joshua's First Riddle

What could it be?
Follow the clues and see.

It looks **round**.
It sounds like **clicking sounds**.
It smells **fruity**.
It feels **hard**.
It tastes like **a strawberry**.

Have you guessed what it could be?
Look below and you will see,
It is...

Answer: An apple.

Joshua Cinar Francisco (4)
Peartree Spring Primary School, Stevenage

Noah's First Riddle

What could it be?
Follow the clues and see.

It looks like **a beach**.
It sounds like **an aeroplane**.
It smells like **fish**.
It feels **hot**.
It tastes like **sausages**.

Have you guessed what it could be?
Look below and you will see,
It is...

Answer: Spain.

Noah Garbutt (4)
Peartree Spring Primary School, Stevenage

Daniel's First Riddle

What could it be?
Follow the clues and see.

It looks like **sand**.
It sounds like **seagulls**.
It smells like **the sea**.
It feels **soft**.
It tastes like **water**.

Have you guessed what it could be?
Look below and you will see,
It is...

Answer: The seaside.

Daniel Tupman (4)
Peartree Spring Primary School, Stevenage

Hazel's First Riddle

What could it be?
Follow the clues and see.

It looks like **little seeds**.
It sounds like **popping**.
It smells **sweet**.
It feels **soft**.
It tastes like **cinnamon**.

Have you guessed what it could be?
Look below and you will see,
It is...

Answer: Popcorn.

Hazel Rose Hurley (4)
Peartree Spring Primary School, Stevenage

Ronnie's First Riddle

What could it be?
Follow the clues and see.

It looks **blue**.
It sounds like *choo, choo.*
It smells like **steam**.
It feels **hard**.
It tastes like **coal**.

Have you guessed what it could be?
Look below and you will see,
It is...

Answer: A train.

Ronnie Wicks (4)
Peartree Spring Primary School, Stevenage

Dylan's First Riddle

What could it be?
Follow the clues and see.

He looks **soft**.
He sounds like **a bang**.
He smells like **radishes**.
He feels **fluffy**.
He tastes like **a carrot**.

Have you guessed who he could be?
Look below and you will see,
He is...

Answer: **Peter Rabbit.**

Dylan O'Driscoll (4)

Peartree Spring Primary School, Stevenage

Alfie's First Riddle

What could it be?
Follow the clues and see.

It looks like **a triangle**.
It sounds **crunchy**.
It smells like **a tomato**.
It feels **crusty**.
It tastes **delicious**.

Have you guessed what it could be?
Look below and you will see,
It is...

Answer: A pizza.

Alfie Stevens (4)
Peartree Spring Primary School, Stevenage

Charlotte's First Riddle

What could it be?
Follow the clues and see.

It looks like **uniform**.
It sounds like **children**.
It smells like **boxes**.
It feels **bumpy**.
It tastes like **snacks**.

Have you guessed what it could be?
Look below and you will see,
It is...

Answer: School.

Charlotte Florence Neal (4)
Peartree Spring Primary School, Stevenage

54

Jake's First Riddle

What could it be?
Follow the clues and see.

It looks like **fun**.
It sounds like **children**.
It smells like **flowers**.
It feels **hard**.
It tastes like **ice cream**.

Have you guessed what it could be?
Look below and you will see,
It is...

Answer: A park.

Jake Knight (4)
Peartree Spring Primary School, Stevenage

Brogan's First Riddle

What could it be?
Follow the clues and see.

It looks like **clothes**.
It sounds like **music**.
It smells like **candles**.
It feels **cold**.
It tastes like **sweets**.

Have you guessed what it could be?
Look below and you will see,
It is...

Answer: Matalan.

Brogan Williams (5)
Peartree Spring Primary School, Stevenage

Jaden's First Riddle

What could it be?
Follow the clues and see.

It looks like **sand**.
It sounds like **the sea**.
It smells like **fish**.
It feels **hot**.
It tastes like **ice cream**.

Have you guessed what it could be?
Look below and you will see,
It is...

Answer: *The beach*.

Jaden Grose (5)
Peartree Spring Primary School, Stevenage

Mollie's First Riddle

What could it be?
Follow the clues and see.

It looks like **a gem**.
It sounds like **sheep**.
It smells like **perfume**.
It feels **soft**.
It tastes like **a lemon**.

Have you guessed what it could be?
Look below and you will see,
It is...

Answer: A mummy.

Mollie Doman (5)
Peartree Spring Primary School, Stevenage

Victor's First Riddle

What could it be?
Follow the clues and see.

It looks **ginormous**.
It sounds like **a roar**.
It smells **nice**.
It feels **hard**.
It tastes like **metal**.

Have you guessed what it could be?
Look below and you will see,
It is...

Answer: A monster truck.

Victor Andrei Marin (5)
Peartree Spring Primary School, Stevenage

Lily's First Riddle

What could it be?
Follow the clues and see.

It looks **red and white**.
It sounds like **ho, ho, ho**.
It smells **sweet**.
It feels **soft**.
It tastes like **candy**.

Have you guessed what it could be?
Look below and you will see,
It is...

Answer: Santa.

Lily Pestana (4)
Peartree Spring Primary School, Stevenage

Mia's First Riddle

What could it be?
Follow the clues and see.

It looks **yellow**.
It sounds like **splash**.
It smells like **ice cream**.
It feels **soft**.
It tastes **crunchy**.

Have you guessed what it could be?
Look below and you will see,
It is...

Answer: *The beach.*

Mia Ramus (4)
Peartree Spring Primary School, Stevenage

Erin's First Riddle

What could it be?
Follow the clues and see.

He looks **red**.
He sounds like **ho, ho, ho**.
He smells like **smoke**.
He feels **fluffy**.
He tastes like **cookies**.

Have you guessed who he could be?
Look below and you will see,
He is...

Answer: Santa.

Erin Usher (5)
Peartree Spring Primary School, Stevenage

Blake's First Riddle

What could it be?
Follow the clues and see.

It looks **yellow**.
It sounds like **nothing**.
It smells like **juice**.
It feels **a bit cold**.
It tastes **yummy**.

Have you guessed what it could be?
Look below and you will see,
It is...

Answer: A lemon.

Blake Bourn (4)
Peartree Spring Primary School, Stevenage

Phoebe's First Riddle

What could it be?
Follow the clues and see.

It looks like **sand**.
It sounds **bubbly**.
It smells like **sand**.
It feels **soft**.
It tastes like **dinner**.

Have you guessed what it could be?
Look below and you will see,
It is...

Answer: *The beach*.

Phoebe Harrison (4)
Peartree Spring Primary School, Stevenage

Noah's First Riddle

What could it be?
Follow the clues and see.

It looks **wiggly**.
It sounds like **worms**.
It smells **good**.
It feels **squishy**.
It tastes like **dinner**.

Have you guessed what it could be?
Look below and you will see,
It is...

Answer: Spaghetti.

Noah Henry Shadbolt (4)
Peartree Spring Primary School, Stevenage

Sophia's First Riddle

What could it be?
Follow the clues and see.

It looks **blue**.
It sounds like **water**.
It smells like **fish**.
It feels **cold**.
It tastes like **water**.

Have you guessed what it could be?
Look below and you will see,
It is...

Answer: *The sea.*

Sophia Lily Sabini (4)
Peartree Spring Primary School, Stevenage

Lydia's First Riddle

What could it be?
Follow the clues and see.

It looks **brown**.
It sounds like **me**.
It smells like **bread**.
It feels **soft**.
It tastes **furry**.

Have you guessed what it could be?
Look below and you will see,
It is...

Answer: A teddy bear.

Lydia Carter (4)
Peartree Spring Primary School, Stevenage

Colby's First Riddle

What could it be?
Follow the clues and see.

It looks **yellow**.
It sounds like **nothing**.
It smells like **bees**.
It feels **round**.
It tastes **sour**.

Have you guessed what it could be?
Look below and you will see,
It is...

Answer: A lemon.

Colby Bridle (5)
Peartree Spring Primary School, Stevenage

Jaycob's First Riddle

What could it be?
Follow the clues and see.

It looks **yellow**.
It sounds like **a crack**.
It smells **yummy**.
It feels **smooth**.
It tastes **fruity**.

Have you guessed what it could be?
Look below and you will see,
It is...

Answer: A banana.

Jaycob Michael Milburn (4)
Peartree Spring Primary School, Stevenage

Frederick's First Riddle

What could it be?
Follow the clues and see.

It looks **juicy**.
It sounds like **nothing**.
It smells **fresh**.
It feels **squishy**.
It tastes **sour**.

Have you guessed what it could be?
Look below and you will see,
It is...

Answer: A lemon.

Frederick Wise (5)
Peartree Spring Primary School, Stevenage

Maddison's First Riddle

What could it be?
Follow the clues and see.

It looks **colourful**.
It sounds **loud**.
It smells like **food**.
It feels **soft**.
It tastes **cold**.

Have you guessed what it could be?
Look below and you will see,
It is...

Answer: *Soft play*.

Maddison Dean (4)
Peartree Spring Primary School, Stevenage

Alfie's First Riddle

What could it be?
Follow the clues and see.

It looks **yellow**.
It sounds **rubbery**.
It smells **yummy**.
It feels **cold**.
It tastes **sweet**.

Have you guessed what it could be?
Look below and you will see,
It is...

Answer: A banana.

Alfie George Green (4)
Peartree Spring Primary School, Stevenage

Maisie's First Riddle

What could it be?
Follow the clues and see.

It looks **brown**.
It sounds **crispy**.
It smells **sweet**.
It feels **cold**.
It tastes **yummy**.

Have you guessed what it could be?
Look below and you will see,
It is...

Answer: Chocolate.

Maisie Chappell (4)
Peartree Spring Primary School, Stevenage

Arabella's First Riddle

What could it be?
Follow the clues and see.

It looks like **fruit**.
It sounds **loud**.
It smells **clean**.
It feels **cold**.
It tastes **yummy**.

Have you guessed what it could be?
Look below and you will see,
It is...

Answer: Asda.

Arabella Garcia-Sevilla (5)
Peartree Spring Primary School, Stevenage

Jamie's First Riddle

This is my riddle about an amazing animal.
What could it be?
Follow the clues to see!

This animal has **stripes** on its body,
And its colours are **orange and black**.
This animal has **four** feet,
It likes **meat** to eat.
The jungle is where it lives,
Its favourite thing to do is **lick his fur**.
This animal has **two** ears,
It makes **roaring** sounds for you to hear.

Are you an animal whizz?
Have you guessed what it is?
It is...

Answer: A tiger.

Jamie Stokoe (5)
Robert Peel Primary School, Sandy

Jackson's First Riddle

This is my riddle about an amazing animal.
What could it be?
Follow the clues to see!

This animal has **spikes** on its body,
And its colour is **red**.
This animal has **four** feet,
It likes **rabbit** to eat.
In a cave is where it lives,
Its favourite thing to do is **breathe fire**.
This animal has **two** ears,
It makes **roar** sounds for you to hear.

Are you an animal whizz?
Have you guessed what it is?
It is...

Answer: A dragon.

Jackson Harper (5)
Robert Peel Primary School, Sandy

Jackson's First Riddle

This is my riddle about an amazing animal.
What could it be?
Follow the clues to see!

This animal has **stripes** on its body,
And its colours are **black and orange**.
This animal has **four** feet,
It likes **meat** to eat.
A jungle is where it lives,
Its favourite thing to do is **hunt**.
This animal has **pointy** ears,
It makes *raaaa* sounds for you to hear.

Are you an animal whizz?
Have you guessed what it is?
It is...

Answer: A tiger.

Jackson Scheibner (4)
Robert Peel Primary School, Sandy

Katie's First Riddle

This is my riddle about an amazing animal.
What could it be?
Follow the clues to see!

This animal has **fur and a tail** on its body,
And its colour is **grey**.
This animal has **four** feet,
It likes **cheese** to eat.
The forest is where it lives,
Its favourite thing to do is **looking for food**.
This animal has **two** ears,
It makes **squeaking** sounds for you to hear.

Are you an animal whizz?
Have you guessed what it is?
It is...

Answer: A rat.

Katie Nemec Vencelova (5)
Robert Peel Primary School, Sandy

Liam's First Riddle

This is my riddle about an amazing animal.
What could it be?
Follow the clues to see!

This animal has **skin and fur** on its body,
And its colours are **orange and black.**
This animal has **four** feet,
It likes **meat** to eat.
In the jungle is where it lives,
Its favourite thing to do is **run.**
This animal has **two** ears,
It makes **roaring** sounds for you to hear.

Are you an animal whizz?
Have you guessed what it is?
It is...

Answer: A tiger.

Liam Kyle Shaw-Chung (5)
Robert Peel Primary School, Sandy

Dotty's First Riddle

This is my riddle about an amazing animal.
What could it be?
Follow the clues to see!

This animal has **fur** on its body,
And its colour is **grey**.
This animal has **four** feet,
It likes **carrots** to eat.
In the fields is where it lives,
Its favourite thing to do is **hop in the fields**.
This animal has **two** ears,
It makes **snuffling** sounds for you to hear.

Are you an animal whizz?
Have you guessed what it is?
It is...

Answer: A rabbit.

Dotty Reading (5)
Robert Peel Primary School, Sandy

Ellie's First Riddle

This is my riddle about an amazing animal.
What could it be?
Follow the clues to see!

This animal has **stripes** on its body,
And its colours are **black and orange**.
This animal has **four** feet,
It likes **meat** to eat.
In a jungle is where it lives,
Its favourite thing to do is **explore**.
This animal has **two** ears,
It makes **roaring** sounds for you to hear.

Are you an animal whizz?
Have you guessed what it is?
It is...

Answer: A tiger.

Ellie Barton (5)
Robert Peel Primary School, Sandy

Sophia's First Riddle

This is my riddle about an amazing animal.
What could it be?
Follow the clues to see!

This animal has **spikes** on its body,
And its colours are **orange and red**.
This animal has **two** feet,
It likes **mice** to eat.
In the jungle is where it lives,
Its favourite thing to do is **roar**.
This animal has **two** ears,
It makes **growling** sounds for you to hear.

Are you an animal whizz?
Have you guessed what it is?
It is...

Answer: A dragon.

Sophia Elizabeth Hurren (5)
Robert Peel Primary School, Sandy

Lucas' First Riddle

This is my riddle about an amazing animal.
What could it be?
Follow the clues to see!

This animal has **yellow stripes** on its body,
And its colour is **green**.
This animal has **no** feet,
It likes **beef** to eat.
A jungle is where it lives,
Its favourite thing to do is **wrap**.
This animal has **no** ears,
It makes **sssss** sounds for you to hear.

Are you an animal whizz?
Have you guessed what it is?
It is...

Answer: A snake.

Lucas English (5)
Robert Peel Primary School, Sandy

Billy's First Riddle

This is my riddle about an amazing animal.
What could it be?
Follow the clues to see!

This animal has **mud** on its body,
And its colour is **pink**.
This animal has **four** feet,
It likes **carrots** to eat.
In the mud is where it lives,
Its favourite thing to do is **jump into the mud**.
This animal has **two** ears,
It makes **oinking** sounds for you to hear.

Are you an animal whizz?
Have you guessed what it is?
It is...

Answer: A pig.

Billy Fry (5)
Robert Peel Primary School, Sandy

George's First Riddle

This is my riddle about an amazing animal.
What could it be?
Follow the clues to see!

This animal has **spikes** on its body,
And its colour is **red**.
This animal has **four** feet,
It likes **meat** to eat.
In the jungle is where it lives,
Its favourite thing to do is **breathe fire**.
This animal has **two** ears,
It makes **roaring** sounds for you to hear.

Are you an animal whizz?
Have you guessed what it is?
It is...

Answer: A dragon.

George Powell-Perry (4)
Robert Peel Primary School, Sandy

Henry's First Riddle

This is my riddle about an amazing animal.
What could it be?
Follow the clues to see!

This animal has **skin** on its body,
And its colour is **red**.
This animal has **four** feet,
It likes **water** to drink.
In the forest is where it lives,
Its favourite thing to do is **blow fire**.
This animal has **two** ears,
It makes **roaring** sounds for you to hear.

Are you an animal whizz?
Have you guessed what it is?
It is...

Answer: A dragon.

Henry Akhurst (5)
Robert Peel Primary School, Sandy

Ernie's First Riddle

This is my riddle about an amazing animal.
What could it be?
Follow the clues to see!

This animal has **a tail** on its body,
And its colour can be **grey**.
This animal has **four** feet,
It likes **carrots** to eat.
A burrow is where it lives,
Its favourite thing to do is **hop**.
This animal has **two** ears,
It makes **sniffing** sounds for you to hear.

Are you an animal whizz?
Have you guessed what it is?
It is...

Answer: A rabbit.

Ernie Eastwood-Ogawa (4)
Robert Peel Primary School, Sandy

Autumn's First Riddle

This is my riddle about an amazing animal.
What could it be?
Follow the clues to see!

This animal has **a tail** on its body,
And its colour is **brown**.
This animal has **four** feet,
It likes **carrots** to eat.
A burrow is where it lives,
Its favourite thing to do is **jump**.
This animal has **two** ears,
It makes **sniffing** sounds for you to hear.

Are you an animal whizz?
Have you guessed what it is?
It is...

Answer: A rabbit.

Autumn Briggs (5)
Robert Peel Primary School, Sandy

Bethanie's First Riddle

This is my riddle about an amazing animal.
What could it be?
Follow the clues to see!

This animal has **some horns** on its body,
And its colour is **brown**.
This animal has **four** feet,
It likes **grass** to eat.
On a farm is where it lives,
Its favourite thing to do is **run about**.
This animal has **two** ears,
It makes **moo** sounds for you to hear.

Are you an animal whizz?
Have you guessed what it is?
It is...

Answer: A cow.

Bethanie Short (5)
Robert Peel Primary School, Sandy

Kian's First Riddle

This is my riddle about an amazing animal.
What could it be?
Follow the clues to see!

This animal has **fur** on its body,
And its colour is **grey**.
This animal has **two** feet,
It likes **bugs** to eat.
In the trees is where it lives,
Its favourite thing to do is **climb**.
This animal has **two** ears,
It makes **ooh, ahh,** sounds for you to hear.

Are you an animal whizz?
Have you guessed what it is?
It is...

Answer: A monkey.

Kian Rogan (5)
Robert Peel Primary School, Sandy

Lewis' First Riddle

This is my riddle about an amazing animal.
What could it be?
Follow the clues to see!

This animal has **fluff** on its body,
And its colour is **brown**.
This animal has **four** feet,
It likes **bones** to eat.
A kennel is where it lives,
Its favourite thing to do is **chase cats**.
This animal has **two** ears,
It makes **woofing** sounds for you to hear.

Are you an animal whizz?
Have you guessed what it is?
It is...

Answer: A dog.

Lewis Geeson-Orsgood (5)
Robert Peel Primary School, Sandy

Elsie's First Riddle

This is my riddle about an amazing animal.
What could it be?
Follow the clues to see!

This animal has **fur** on its body,
And its colour is **grey**.
This animal has **four** feet,
It likes **cabbage** to eat.
In a field is where it lives,
Its favourite thing to do is **jump**.
This animal has **two** ears,
It makes **squeaky** sounds for you to hear.

Are you an animal whizz?
Have you guessed what it is?
It is...

Answer: A rabbit.

Elsie Rowley (5)
Robert Peel Primary School, Sandy

Penny's First Riddle

This is my riddle about an amazing animal.
What could it be?
Follow the clues to see!

This animal has **hair** on its body,
And its colour is **grey**.
This animal has **four** feet,
It likes **mud** to eat.
On a farm is where it lives,
Its favourite thing to do is **lie in mud**.
This animal has **two** ears,
It makes **oinking** sounds for you to hear.

Are you an animal whizz?
Have you guessed what it is?
It is...

Answer: A pig.

Penny Wallace (4)

Robert Peel Primary School, Sandy

Kaitlyn's First Riddle

This is my riddle about an amazing animal.
What could it be?
Follow the clues to see!

This animal has **hair** on its body,
And its colour is **brown**.
This animal has **four** feet,
It likes **apples** to eat.
On a farm is where it lives,
Its favourite thing to do is **run**.
This animal has **two** ears,
It makes **neighing** sounds for you to hear.

Are you an animal whizz?
Have you guessed what it is?
It is...

Answer: A horse.

Kaitlyn Merrett (4)
Robert Peel Primary School, Sandy

Kai's First Riddle

This is my riddle about an amazing animal.
What could it be?
Follow the clues to see!

This animal has **horns** on its body,
And its colour is **brown**.
This animal has **four** feet,
It likes **grass** to eat.
On a farm is where it lives,
Its favourite thing to do is **sleep**.
This animal has **two** ears,
It makes **moo** sounds for you to hear.

Are you an animal whizz?
Have you guessed what it is?
It is...

Answer: An ox.

Kai James Parks (5)
Robert Peel Primary School, Sandy

Ebony's First Riddle

This is my riddle about an amazing animal.
What could it be?
Follow the clues to see!

This animal has **hair** on its body,
And its colour is **brown**.
This animal has **four** feet,
It likes **grass** to eat.
On a farm is where it lives,
Its favourite thing to do is **run**.
This animal has **two** ears,
It makes **neighing** sounds for you to hear.

Are you an animal whizz?
Have you guessed what it is?
It is...

Answer: A horse.

Ebony Chalkley (5)
Robert Peel Primary School, Sandy

Ashlee's First Riddle

This is my riddle about an amazing animal.
What could it be?
Follow the clues to see!

This animal has **legs** on its body,
And its colour is **brown**.
This animal has **four** feet,
It likes **grass** to eat.
On a farm is where it lives,
Its favourite thing to do is **run**.
This animal has **two** ears,
It makes **neighing** sounds for you to hear.

Are you an animal whizz?
Have you guessed what it is?
It is...

Answer: A horse.

Ashlee Fielding (5)
Robert Peel Primary School, Sandy

Tanya's First Riddle

This is my riddle about an amazing animal.
What could it be?
Follow the clues to see!

This animal has **fur** on its body,
And its colour is **ginger**.
This animal has **four** feet,
It likes **bones** to eat.
In a kennel is where it lives,
Its favourite thing to do is **woof**.
This animal has **two** ears,
It makes **woofing** sounds for you to hear.

Are you an animal whizz?
Have you guessed what it is?
It is...

Answer: A dog.

Tanya Lovett (5)

Robert Peel Primary School, Sandy

Mylo's First Riddle

This is my riddle about an amazing animal.
What could it be?
Follow the clues to see!

This animal has **a beautiful** body,
And its colour is **green**.
This animal has **zero** feet,
It likes **grass** to eat.
In a jungle is where it lives,
Its favourite thing to do is **sleep**.
This animal has **zero** ears,
It makes **sss** sounds for you to hear.

Are you an animal whiz?
Have you guessed what it is?
It is...

Answer: A snake.

Mylo James Darrington (4)
Robert Peel Primary School, Sandy

Rylee's First Riddle

This is my riddle about an amazing animal.
What could it be?
Follow the clues to see!

This animal has **hair** on its body,
And its colour is **brown**.
This animal has **four** feet,
It likes **bones** to eat.
In a house is where it lives,
Its favourite thing to do is **bark**.
This animal has **two** ears,
It makes **woofing** sounds for you to hear.

Are you an animal whizz?
Have you guessed what it is?
It is...

Answer: A dog.

Rylee Bayford (4)
Robert Peel Primary School, Sandy

Max's First Riddle

This is my riddle about an amazing animal.
What could it be?
Follow the clues to see!

This animal has **scales** on its body,
And its colour is **green**.
This animal has **no** feet,
It likes **trees** to eat.
In the woods is where it lives,
Its favourite thing to do is **eat**.
This animal has **two** ears,
It makes **sss** sounds for you to hear.

Are you an animal whizz?
Have you guessed what it is?
It is...

Answer: A snake.

Max Xander Whytock (5)
Robert Peel Primary School, Sandy

Devon's First Riddle

This is my riddle about an amazing animal.
What could it be?
Follow the clues to see!

This animal has stripes on its body,
And its colours are **orange and black**.
This animal has **four** feet,
It likes **meat** to eat.
The forest is where it lives,
Its favourite thing to do is **bite**.
This animal has **two** ears,
It makes **a roar** sounds for you to hear.

Are you an animal whizz?
Have you guessed what it is?
It is...

Answer: A tiger.

Devon Huckle (5)
Robert Peel Primary School, Sandy

Jace's First Riddle

This is my riddle about an amazing animal.
What could it be?
Follow the clues to see!

This animal has **fur** on its body,
And its colour is **grey**.
This animal has **four** feet,
It likes **cheese** to eat.
A house is where it lives,
Its favourite thing to do is **chew**.
This animal has **two** ears,
It makes **squeaking** sounds for you to hear.

Are you an animal whizz?
Have you guessed what it is?
It is...

Answer: A rat.

Jace Quan (5)
Robert Peel Primary School, Sandy

Chloe's First Riddle

This is my riddle about an amazing animal.
What could it be?
Follow the clues to see!

This animal has **fur** on its body,
And its colour is **brown**.
This animal has **four** feet,
It likes **hay** to eat.
On a farm is where it lives,
Its favourite thing to do is **run**.
This animal has **two** ears,
It makes **neighing** sounds for you to hear.

Are you an animal whizz?
Have you guessed what it is?
It is...

Answer: A horse.

Chloe Louise Butler (5)
Robert Peel Primary School, Sandy

Marley's First Riddle

This is my riddle about an amazing animal.
What could it be?
Follow the clues to see!

This animal has **fur** on its body,
And its colour is **brown**.
This animal has **four** feet,
It likes **cheese** to eat.
In a hole is where it lives,
Its favourite thing to do is **eat**.
This animal has **two** ears,
It makes **squeaky** sounds for you to hear.

Are you an animal whizz?
Have you guessed what it is?
It is...

Answer: A rat.

Marley Berney (4)
Robert Peel Primary School, Sandy

Jack's First Riddle

This is my riddle about an amazing animal.
What could it be?
Follow the clues to see!

This animal has **fur** on its body,
And its colour is **black**.
This animal has **four** feet,
It likes **grass** to eat.
On a farm is where it lives,
Its favourite thing to do is **sit**.
This animal has **two** ears,
It makes **moo** sounds for you to hear.

Are you an animal whizz?
Have you guessed what it is?
It is...

Answer: An ox.

Jack Quan (5)
Robert Peel Primary School, Sandy

Luca's First Riddle

This is my riddle about an amazing animal.
What could it be?
Follow the clues to see!

This animal has **hair** on its body,
And its colour is **white**.
This animal has **four** feet,
It likes **hay** to eat.
A farm is where it lives,
Its favourite thing to do is **run**.
This animal has **two** ears,
It makes **neigh** sounds for you to hear.

Are you an animal whizz?
Have you guessed what it is?
It is...

Answer: A horse.

Luca Gatti (4)
Robert Peel Primary School, Sandy

Henry's First Riddle

What could it be?
Follow the clues and see.

It looks like **a man**.
It sounds like **crunchy leaves**.
It smells like **a delicious snack**.
It feels like **a biscuit**.
It tastes like **ginger**.

Have you guessed what it could be?
Look below and you will see,
It is...

Answer: A gingerbread man.

Henry Amies (5)
Sheerhatch Primary School, Willington

Phoebe's First Riddle

What could it be?
Follow the clues and see.

It looks like **little clouds**.
It sounds like *pop, pop, pop*.
It smells like **the cinema**.
It feels **bumpy**.
It tastes **sweet**.

Have you guessed what it could be?
Look below and you will see,
It is...

Answer: Popcorn.

Phoebe Rae Clark (4)
Sheerhatch Primary School, Willington

Olivia's First Riddle

What could it be?
Follow the clues and see.

It looks like **a flying saucer**.
It sounds like *munch, munch*.
It smells like **meat**.
It feels **squidgy**.
It tastes **yummy**.

Have you guessed what it could be?
Look below and you will see,
It is...

Answer: A burger.

Olivia Rodgers (4)
Sheerhatch Primary School, Willington

Oliver's First Riddle

What could it be?
Follow the clues and see.

It looks like **a dark room**.
It sounds like **shouting**.
It smells like **sweets**.
It feels **exciting**.
It tastes like **popcorn**.

Have you guessed what it could be?
Look below and you will see,
It is...

Answer: A cinema.

Oliver Anderson (5)
Sheerhatch Primary School, Willington

Ginny's First Riddle

What could it be?
Follow the clues and see.

It looks like **a sausage in a bun**.
It sounds **quiet**.
It smells like **onions**.
It feels **smooth**.
It tastes like **red sauce**.

Have you guessed what it could be?
Look below and you will see,
It is...

Answer: A hot dog.

Ginny Fitzgerald (5)
Sheerhatch Primary School, Willington

Grace's First Riddle

What could it be?
Follow the clues and see.

It looks like **a cloud**.
It has **no sound**.
It smells like **sweets**.
It feels **sticky**.
It tastes like **sugar**.

Have you guessed what it could be?
Look below and you will see,
It is...

Answer: Candyfloss.

Grace Mary Beales (5)
Sheerhatch Primary School, Willington

Mathilda's First Riddle

What could it be?
Follow the clues and see.

It looks like **pink and purple balloons**.
It sounds like **fun magic**.
It smells like **cake and candles**.
It feels like **balloons and string**.
It tastes like **sweets**.

Have you guessed what it could be?
Look below and you will see,
It is...

Answer: A birthday party.

Mathilda Walters (4)
St Bartholomew's CE Primary School, Wiggington

Jessica's First Riddle

What could it be?
Follow the clues and see.

It looks like **crashing waves**.
It sounds like **screeching seagulls**.
It smells like **salty water**.
It feels like **warm sand**.
It tastes like **ice cream**.

Have you guessed what it could be?
Look below and you will see,
It is...

Answer: On the beach.

Jessica Cubitt (4)
St Bartholomew's CE Primary School, Wiggington

Amelie's First Riddle

What could it be?
Follow the clues and see.

It looks like **children bouncing**.
It sounds like **music**.
It smells like **sausages and burgers**.
It feels like **fun**.
It tastes like **lollies**.

Have you guessed what it could be?
Look below and you will see,
It is...

Answer: A garden party.

Amelie Ryan-Clark (5)
St Bartholomew's CE Primary School, Wiggington

Tia's First Riddle

What could it be?
Follow the clues and see.

It looks like **sunshine**.
It sounds like **crashing waves**.
It smells like **suncream**.
It feels like **seashells**.
It tastes like **ice cream**.

Have you guessed what it could be?
Look below and you will see,
It is...

Answer: **At the beach.**

Tia Arthur (4)
St Bartholomew's CE Primary School, Wiggington

Carlton's First Riddle

What could it be?
Follow the clues and see.

It looks like **green grass**.
It sounds like **splashing**.
It smells like **sausages**.
It feels like **grass**.
It tastes like **burgers**.

Have you guessed what it could be?
Look below and you will see,
It is...

Answer: A garden party.

Carlton Maclaughlin (5)
St Bartholomew's CE Primary School, Wiggington

118

Catherine's First Riddle

What could it be?
Follow the clues and see.

It looks like **a dinosaur**.
It sounds like **screaming**.
It smells like **cheese**.
It feels like **learning**.
It tastes like **milk**.

Have you guessed what it could be?
Look below and you will see,
It is...

Answer: Being in class.

Catherine Reading-Burgos (5)
St Bartholomew's CE Primary School, Wiggington

Polly's First Riddle

What could it be?
Follow the clues and see.

It looks like **cake**.
It sounds like **shouting**.
It smells like **cucumber**.
It feels like **balloons**.
It tastes like **juice**.

Have you guessed what it could be?
Look below and you will see,
It is...

Answer: A birthday party.

Polly Goodman (5)
St Bartholomew's CE Primary School, Wiggington

Jessica's First Riddle

What could it be?
Follow the clues and see.

It looks like **balloons**.
It sounds like **music**.
It smells like **flowers**.
It feels like **grass**.
It tastes like **muffins**.

Have you guessed what it could be?
Look below and you will see,
It is...

Answer: A garden party.

Jessica Beeley (5)
St Bartholomew's CE Primary School, Wiggington

Ollie's First Riddle

What could it be?
Follow the clues and see.

It looks like **a present**.
It sounds like **playing**.
It smells like **cake**.
It feels like **fun**.
It tastes like **jelly**.

Have you guessed what it could be?
Look below and you will see,
It is...

Answer: A birthday party.

Ollie White (4)
St Bartholomew's CE Primary School, Wiggington

Euan's First Riddle

What could it be?
Follow the clues and see.

It looks like **crabs**.
It sounds like **the sea**.
It smells **fishy**.
It feels like **the sand**.
It tastes like **ice cream**.

Have you guessed what it could be?
Look below and you will see,
It is...

Answer: *At the beach.*

Euan Rhys-Davies (5)
St Bartholomew's CE Primary School, Wiggington

Oscar's First Riddle

What could it be?
Follow the clues and see.

It looks like **sunny**.
It sounds like **waves**.
It smells like **fish**.
It feels like **hot sand**.
It tastes like **hot dogs**.

Have you guessed what it could be?
Look below and you will see,
It is...

Answer: *The beach.*

Oscar Peter Cadman (4)
St Bartholomew's CE Primary School, Wiggington

Jess' First Riddle

What could it be?
Follow the clues and see.

It looks like **a white ball with a carrot and coal poking out.**
It sounds like **swish** (when knocked over).
It smells like **carrots.**
It feels **cold, soft and wet.**
It tastes like **carrot ice cream.**

Have you guessed what it could be?
Look below and you will see,
It is...

Answer: A snowman.

Jess Limburn (5)
St Mary's Infant School, Baldock

Mercedes' First Riddle

What could it be?
Follow the clues and see.

It looks like **different shapes**.
It sounds like **a noisy jingle**.
It smells like **it's been in someone's pocket**.
It feels like **very rough and sometimes heavy**.
It tastes like **hard and dirty**.

Have you guessed what it could be?
Look below and you will see,
It is...

Answer: Money.

Mercedes Woods (5)
St Mary's Infant School, Baldock

Albie's First Riddle

What could it be?
Follow the clues and see.

It looks like **an orange with eyes**.
It sounds like **spooky noises**.
It smells like **something that's a bit sweet**.
It feels like **something hard**.
It tastes like **Halloween**.

Have you guessed what it could be?
Look below and you will see,
It is...

Answer: A pumpkin.

Albie Cardall (4)
St Mary's Infant School, Baldock

Freddie's First Riddle

What could it be?
Follow the clues and see.

It looks like **a big stick**.
It sounds like *crash, crash*.
It smells like **wood**.
It feels like **bumpy and hard**.
It tastes like**... I've only had a chocolate one**.

Have you guessed what it could be?
Look below and you will see,
It is...

Answer: A log.

Freddie Rowe (4)
St Mary's Infant School, Baldock

Edith's First Riddle

What could it be?
Follow the clues and see.

It looks like **a circle**.
It sounds like **a 'p'**.
It smells like **sweets**.
It feels **hard on the outside, squishy on the inside**.
It tastes **sweet and savoury**.

Have you guessed what it could be?
Look below and you will see,
It is...

Answer: A pumpkin.

Edith Lewis (5)
St Mary's Infant School, Baldock

James' First Riddle

What could it be?
Follow the clues and see.

It looks like **a circle**.
It sounds like *crunch, crunch*.
It smells like **the fresh outside**.
It feels like **a cold ball**.
It tastes like **sweet juice**.

Have you guessed what it could be?
Look below and you will see,
It is...

Answer: An apple.

James Taylor (5)
St Mary's Infant School, Baldock

Evie's First Riddle

What could it be?
Follow the clues and see.

It looks like **a ball**.
It sounds like **trouble**.
It smells like **a clean plate**.
It feels like **water**.
It tastes like **soap**.

Have you guessed what it could be?
Look below and you will see,
It is...

Answer: A bubble.

Evie Jane Fleming-Smales (5)
St Mary's Infant School, Baldock

YOUNG WRITERS INFORMATION

We hope you have enjoyed reading this book – and that you will continue to in the coming years.

If you're a young writer who enjoys reading and creative writing, or the parent of an enthusiastic poet or story writer, do visit our website **www.youngwriters.co.uk**. Here you will find free competitions, workshops and games, as well as recommended reads, a poetry glossary and our blog. There's lots to keep budding writers motivated to write!

If you would like to order further copies of this book, or any of our other titles, then please give us a call or order via your online account.

Young Writers
Remus House
Coltsfoot Drive
Peterborough
PE2 9BF
(01733) 890066
info@youngwriters.co.uk

Join in the conversation!
Tips, news, giveaways and much more!

 YoungWritersUK    @YoungWritersCW